FUN AND GAMES
with the
RECORDER
TUTOR **1** BOOK

Method for descant recorder

Gerhard Engel · **Gudrun Heyens**

Konrad Hünteler · **Hans-Martin Linde**

Translated and adapted by Peter Bowman

With illustrations
by Julie Beech and John Minnion

ED 12590 · ISMN M-2201-1909-5

SCHOTT

Acknowledgments

The publishers would like to thank the staff and pupils of
Yerbury School, London, for allowing us to take the colour
photographs.

Thanks, in particular, to Jean Minnion, Simon McChesney,
Alexandra Antoniou, Joe Lorber, Kiyo Matsui, Cassie Purcell,
Cartelle Thomas, Thomas Willmore and Mathilda Wright-
Sutherland.

Thanks also to Julie Beech for letting us include her mural in
the photo on page 17.

ED 12590

British Library Cataloguing-in-Publication Data. A catalogue
record for this book is available from the British Library.

ISMN M-2201-1909-5

Cover illustrations   Julie Beech

Text illustrations   Julie Beech, John Minnion

Design   The Design Works, Reading

Colour photos
Maria de Fatima Campos (Copyright and moral rights
reserved by Campos and Davis Photos 1998)

Black and white photos
Volker Kaiser, H. J. Kropp, Iris Christmann

Music setting   Halstan & Co.

My recorder

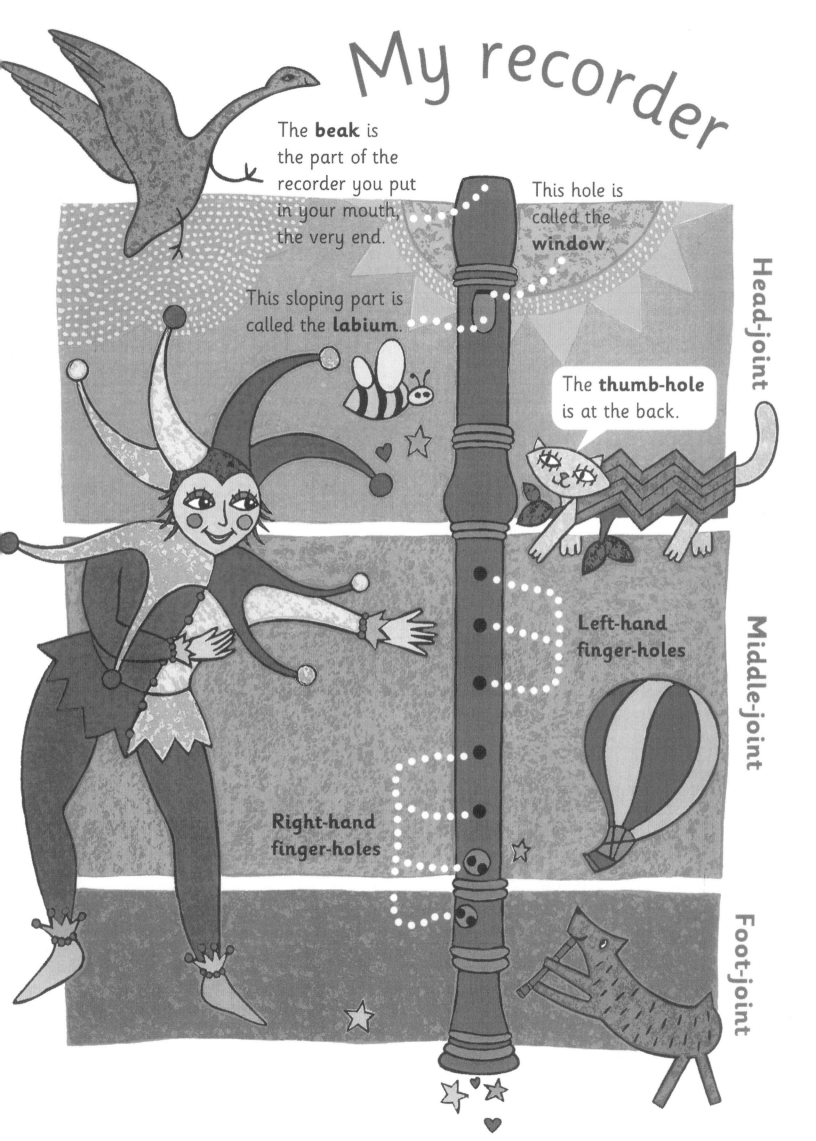

The **beak** is the part of the recorder you put in your mouth, the very end.

This hole is called the **window**.

This sloping part is called the **labium**.

The **thumb-hole** is at the back.

Left-hand finger-holes

Right-hand finger-holes

Head-joint

Middle-joint

Foot-joint

Foreword

Dear Parents and Teachers

Fun and Games with the Recorder is a comprehensive recorder tutor covering all stages from the first notes of the beginner up to the point of professional instruction for budding performers. Although the recorder is often the instrument with which children make their first musical discoveries, it is also an instrument of the highest artistic merit. This series of books tries to link these two extremes, providing a carefully-planned pathway between first, playful contact with the instrument and professional recorder playing.

The three **Tutor Books** are suitable for use both with small groups and for individual tuition. Progress is methodical and is made in small steps placing great value on consistent work with breathing, sound production and the development of rhythmic security.

In the **Tutor Books** we speak directly to the child and provide carefully planned, precisely formulated exercises. We recognise that some children learning the recorder will not yet be able to read, but hope that this will provide an opportunity for a parent or teacher to become involved in the learning process. Each step in this process should be fun and accessible to both the parent/teacher and the child.

Tutor Book 1 is intended for children from about six years of age. Previous musical experience is not essential but undoubtedly would prove useful. It concentrates on the notes B^1, A^1, G^1, E^1, C^2 and D^2, leaving sufficient time and space for the development of articulation, rhythmic security and breathing techniques. **Tutor Book 2** adds the notes C^1, D^1, F^1, E^2, F^2 and B flat, whilst **Tutor Book 3** completes the range up to C^3 – at which point the treble recorder can be introduced.

Tutor Books 1, **2** and **3** are complemented by Tune Books 1, 2 and 3. The Tune Books are matched to the stages of the learning process of the **Tutor Books** and provide additional practice pieces and exercises, sometimes with accompaniment.

In the **Teacher's Commentary** we explain the teaching methodology behind the tutor and provide stimulation for ideas for lessons.

It will be helpful if the child has a manuscript book of her or his own, or some manuscript paper. Dotty's Note Book (ED 12641) is specially designed for the purpose, with large staves suitable for children as well as plain pages for words and pictures.

We wish users of this tutor every success and happiness with their recorder playing.

T = refer to the Tune Book   **C** = refer to the **Teacher's Commentary**

Contents

Holding the recorder

C A good **body position** is important...

... and so is a good **hand position**

Draw or paint a picture of your recorder.

Beginning is easy

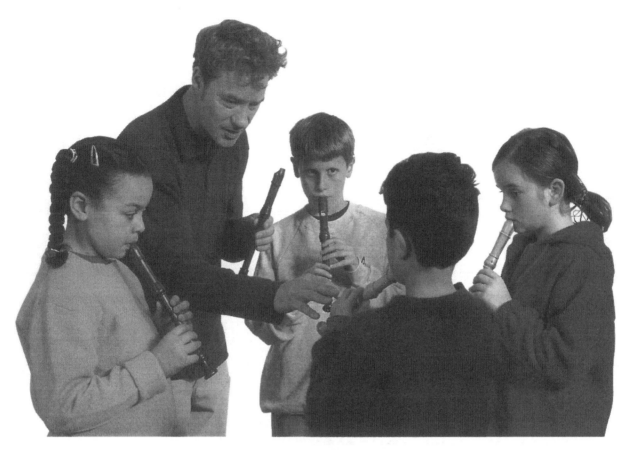

c Try out your recorder
to see how it sounds.
Try not to play too loudly
or too softly!

Recorder song

Prac – tise   my   re – cor – der   gai – ly,   sound – ing   bet – ter,   learn – ing   dai – ly!

From noise to note

c Some notes sound like a wailing cat.

Here's a way a cat sound could be drawn:

Other notes sound like a siren:

Draw a 'siren' note:

When you play tunes you don't usually want to sound like a siren or a wailing cat. A good note for playing tunes can be drawn like this:

What is the difference between the cat or siren sounds and the good note for playing tunes?

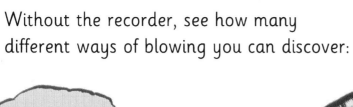

◧ Blowing exercises

Without the recorder, see how many
different ways of blowing you can discover:

**You could blow
beautiful big
soap bubbles.**

**You could blow
out a candle.**

**See how long
you can keep
a feather in
the air.**

**Breathe against
a mirror and see
if you can make
a big misty patch
with your breath.**

How do you need to blow down the recorder to play a firm, even note?

◧ Cotton wool game

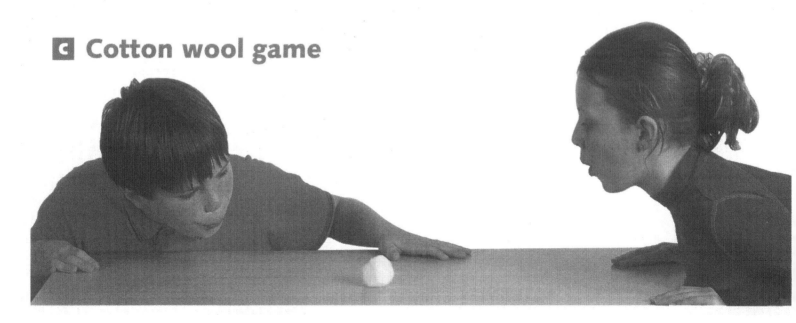

Dotty-do-a-lot

C Now it gets even more interesting...

The best sound on the recorder always has a clear beginning.

Silently blow a 'do' against the palm of your hand and imagine a beautiful strong, long note.

Now use your recorder to blow some notes beginning with 'do'. Make sure your hand and body positions are correct. Notice the way your tongue moves.

Dotty-do-a-lot is here to remind us that every note must begin with a gentle 'do'.

C Telephone game

When we lift the receiver we hear a long tone:

dooo _____

When we have dialled and the phone at the other end rings, we hear:

do ___ **do** _____ **do** ___ **do** _____ **do** ___ **do** _____ **do** ___ **do**

If the line is engaged, we hear lots of short notes:

do ___ **do** ___ **do** ___ **do** ___ **do** ___ **do** ___ **do** ___ **do** ___

Let's phone Grandma:

Dooo _____

I	dial	the	num -	bers	1	2	3
to	ask	if	Gran	will	come	to	tea.
Do	do	do	is	all	I	hear,	
Grand - ma's	on	the	phone.	Oh	dear!		

11

Who's playing 'do'?

c Everyone takes turns to make as many sounds as they can: cat, siren, kettle, owl or 'do'.

The others listen and try to spot Dotty's 'do'.

Finger game for the left hand

C Touch your thumb and index finger together like this:

Try to do the same with your other fingers:
- your thumb and middle finger
- your thumb and third finger.

Can you touch together your thumb and your little finger?

Stroke your finger pads together lightly, keeping your fingers relaxed and curved.

With your left hand at the top of your recorder, stroke the finger-holes until they are fully covered by your thumb and index finger like this:

Now blow into your recorder and play a note, remembering to start with 'do'.

When you can make a good sound, play the 'Recorder song' again.

C 1 Recorder song

Pract – ice   my   re – cor – der   gai – ly,   sound – ing   bet – ter,   learn – ing   dai – ly!

C 2 The surprise!

When   I   sit   to   play   once   more,   gig – gles   come   up   from   the   floor.

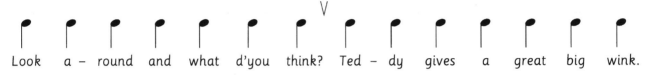

Look   a – round   and   what   d'you   think?   Ted – dy   gives   a   great   big   wink.

'V' is a breath mark. It shows the best place to take a breath.

Recorder accompaniment

- The recorder should sit loosely on your lower lip.
- It shouldn't touch your teeth.
- Your lips should close lightly around the end of the mouthpiece (the beak).
- Don't let the recorder become wet.

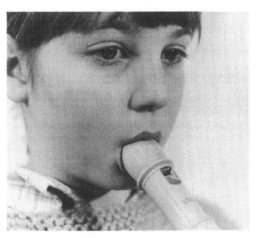

Correct position   **Wrong position**

Look in a mirror to check your recorder position.

3 Cat's song

Group 1

Mi - aow!   Mi - aow!   Mi - aow!   Mi - aow!

Group 2

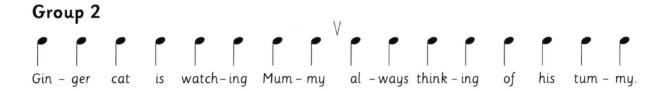

Gin – ger   cat   is   watch–ing   Mum – my   al –ways think–ing   of   his   tum – my.

Group 1

Mi - aow!   Mi - aow!

Group 2

Mum puts cream out   in   a   pot.   Naugh–ty   cat! He's drunk the   lot!

Recorder accompaniment

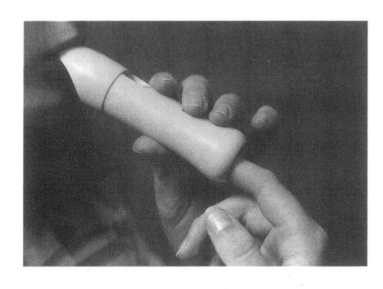

You can 'miaow' with
your recorder like this.

15

Long and short notes

Your teacher will play some long and short notes, like before, pretending to be a telephone.

Listen carefully!

Write down what you have heard in the box below:

Did you notice that the long notes played by your teacher were twice as long as the short ones?

Long notes _____   _____   _____

Short notes __   __   __   __   __   __

Now think up your own pattern of long notes and short notes and write it down:

When you play the next four pieces, take care that the long notes last twice as long as the short ones.

4 Short and long notes

This   old   man,   he   played   one,   he   played   nick   nack   on   my   drum.

5 Red jelly

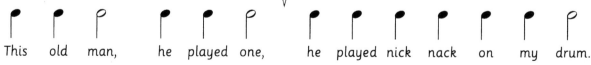

Red   jel – ly,   green   jel – ly,   eat   it   all   up,   full   bel – ly.

6 On the platform

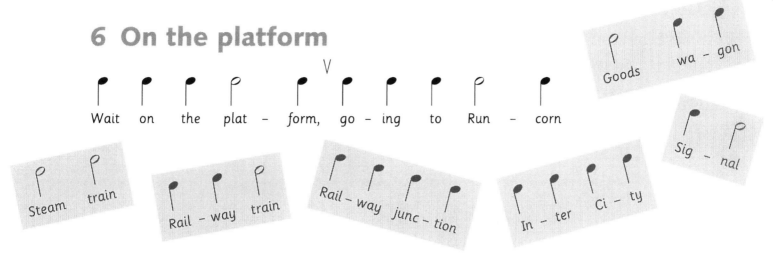

Wait on the plat - form, go - ing to Run - corn

Goods wa - gon

Sig - nal

Steam train

Rail - way train

Rail - way junc - tion

In - ter Ci - ty

7 The train game

Rail - way train, rail - way train. Who will join the great big train?

How to play the train game

One of you is the engine and the others are the carriages.

Place your hands on the shoulders of the person in front.

Setting off on the left foot, the train steams through the room. Everyone says 'ch - ch - ch...' and, when the train is at full steam, 'Rail-way train, rail-way train, who will join the great big train?'

Did you notice that in this game you always take two footsteps on the word 'train'? You can silently count 'one, two' when you play long notes, and 'one' when you play short notes.

Practise and then play:

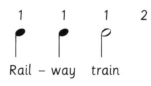

1   1   1   2

Rail - way train

Play and count again through the pieces on the opposite page and the top of this one. Write the correct numbers over the notes.

Invent a piece of music using short and long notes, then write it out using ♪ and 𝅝.

Put breath marks in all the right places!
Think carefully about the correct way to hold your recorder when you play,
and how to blow 'do'.

C Echo game

Take your recorder apart
and try to play an echo game
using only the head-joint.

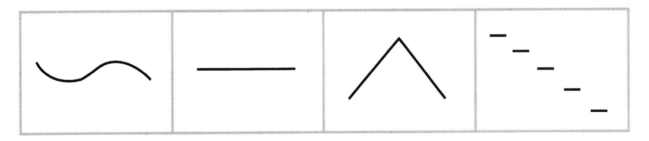

One person plays a sound and the others try one by one to copy it.
There is no limit to the sound shapes you can make.
Don't forget to swap roles so that everyone has a turn
at inventing a sound shape.

The note B

c Music can be written down using five lines called **staff**.

The note **B** lies exactly in the middle, on the third line.

We already know that there are short and long notes.

They are called **crotchets** and **minims**.

Write down the **B** on the **staves** below, first as a crotchet and then as a minim.

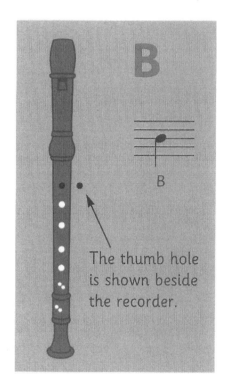

The thumb hole is shown beside the recorder.

1
crotchet

1 2
minim

Play the two pieces on page 16 again, and then write them down below.

When you play, don't forget the '**do**'.

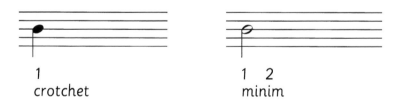

This   old   man,   he   played   one,   he   played   nick   nack   on   my   drum.

Red   jel – ly, green   jel – ly,   eat   it   all   up,   full   bel – ly.

19

A thin line followed by a thick line normally shows that you have reached the end of a piece of music. Look out for this in the following pieces.

8 Playing in twos

Piano accompaniment...

Brian Bonsor
Arranged by G.H.

...or treble recorder accompaniment

The note A

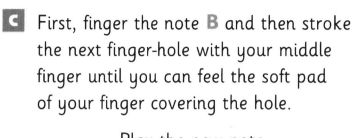

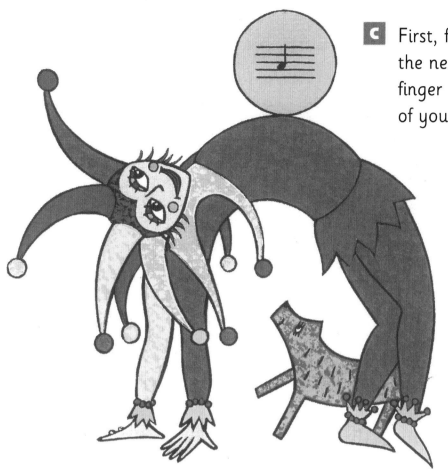

C First, finger the note **B** and then stroke the next finger-hole with your middle finger until you can feel the soft pad of your finger covering the hole.

Play the new note.
It is called **A**.

Does it sound higher or lower than the **B**?

B   A

The **A** is written directly under the **B** line in the space between the two lines.

Now play the note **A**:

as crotchets   do ___ do ___ do ___ do ___

1

as minims   do _____   do _____

1   2

Now write the note **A** yourself, as a crotchet and as a minim.

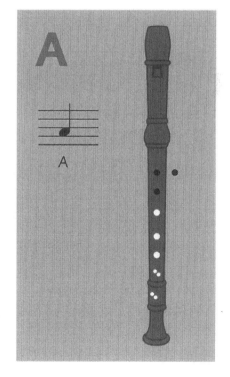

1
crotchet

1   2
minim

Flower name game

Here are some flower names.
Play them carefully, remembering '**do**'.
Make the minims last twice as long
as the crotchets.

but – ter – cup

dan – de – li – on

sun – flow – er

tu – lip

dai – sy

daf – fo – dil

rose

Do you know any other flowers?
Write their names and notes below, using crotchets and minims.

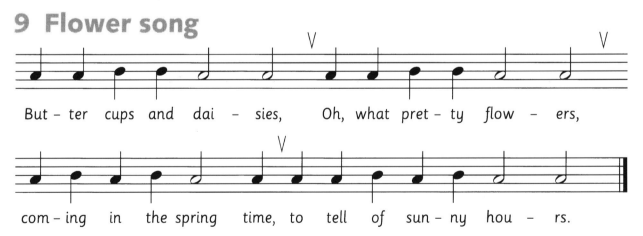

9 Flower song

But – ter cups and dai – sies, Oh, what pret – ty flow – ers,

com – ing in the spring time, to tell of sun – ny hou – rs.

Invent a melody:

Daf – fo – dil, daf – fo – dil, bloom – ing when the wind is chill.

10 My goldfish

Music: G.E.
Words: L.C. & W.L.

I have four big gold – fish help – ing me to prac – tise.

As they swim they seem to say, 'It's great fun to hear you play!'

11 Little piece

Brian Bonsor/G.H.

Piano accompaniment

Brian Bonsor/G.H.

Sound games
and listening games

c Bird song

Here are some ways you can make bird song sounds using the head-joint of your recorder. See if you can invent some more of your own.

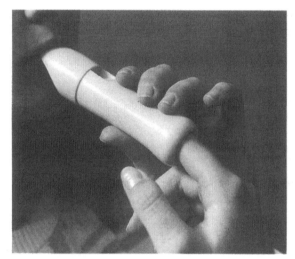

Put your index finger in the head-joint.

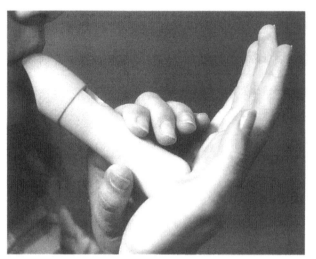

Cover the head-joint with your hand.

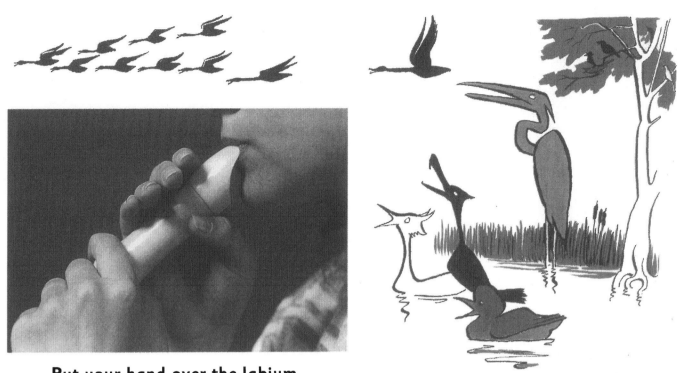

Put your hand over the labium.

Write down your bird song. Then listen carefully while others play and write down some of their bird songs too.

Weather game

c Make these weather sounds using both the head-joint and the whole recorder.

Rain

Hail

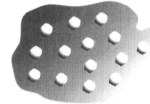

Thunder storm

Snow

Gentle breeze

Howling gale

Now make the sound of a siren, a frightened little bird, and a cat stuck in a tree.

Make up a story using all of your sounds. Draw your story in the box, then play it with your friends.

At home, play the piece again either alone or with friends.

Invent new sounds and new stories. Try using other instruments (e.g. from the kitchen).

The note G
and the treble clef

G

G

C First, finger and play an **A**.
Then place your third finger on
the next hole.

When you can feel that the pad of
your finger is completely covering
the hole, blow '**do**'.

The new note is called **G**.

Finger and play both notes,
one after the other.

Compare **G** with the notes
A and **B**.

The **A** sounds lower than the **B**
and therefore is written lower.

The **G** sounds lower than the **A**.

Add the note **G** below.

B   A   G

The treble clef

The **treble clef** sign is used when
music for voices or high pitched
instruments such as the recorder
and the violin are written down.

Sometimes the treble clef is called
the **G** clef because it circles around
the **G** line.

Complete the clefs below, then draw
some more next to them.

Exercises with G

Write the note name under every note.

12

13

Invent your own exercise

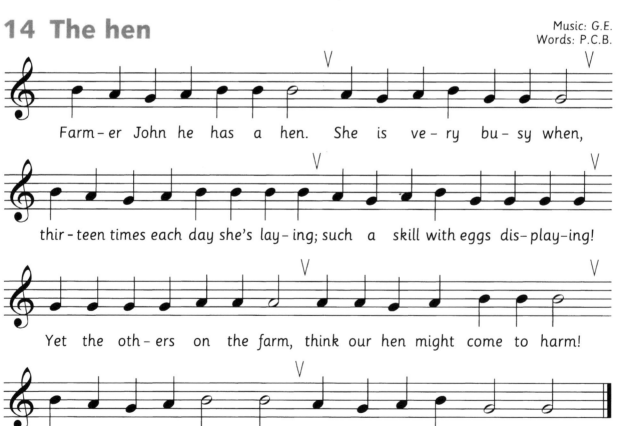

14 The hen

Music: G.E.
Words: P.C.B.

Farm-er John he has a hen. She is ve-ry bu-sy when,

thir-teen times each day she's lay-ing; such a skill with eggs dis-play-ing!

Yet the oth-ers on the farm, think our hen might come to harm!

Dai-ly eggs a-lay - ing. Still, she's not com-plain - ing.

© 1999 Schott & Co. Ltd, London

28

Bar-lines and time-signatures

Music is made up of lots of different kinds of notes. It's easy to get them muddled!

So that this doesn't happen, we split them up into groups.
Each group lasts exactly the same length of time.
The first note of each group is played or sung with more emphasis than the other notes in the group.

We draw **bar-lines** down through the staff directly before each note that is to be emphasized. This separates the groups of notes into **bars**.

Look carefully at the next song, 'Polly Flinders'. Discover where the emphasis lies and draw in the bar-lines.

15 Polly Flinders

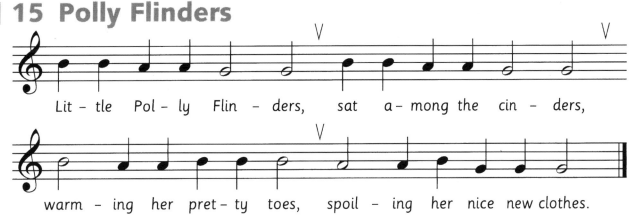

Lit – tle Pol – ly Flin – ders, sat a – mong the cin – ders,

warm – ing her pret – ty toes, spoil – ing her nice new clothes.

How many crotchets are there in each bar?

The number of crotchets in each bar tells us the **time-signature**.

When there are four crotchets in each bar, as in 'Polly Flinders', we call the time signature **four-four** time, and we show it like this:

29

Write in the **time-signature** and draw the **bar-lines** for 'The cuckoo':

16 The cuckoo

Nursery rhyme
Setting: P.C.B.

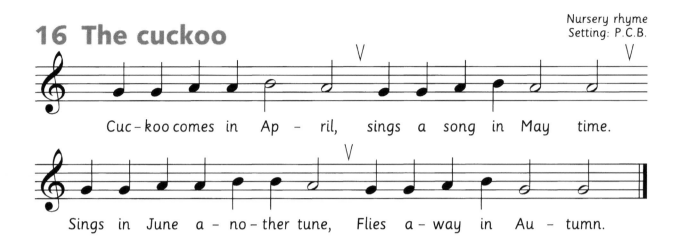

Cuc – koo comes in Ap – ril, sings a song in May time.

Sings in June a – no – ther tune, Flies a – way in Au – tumn.

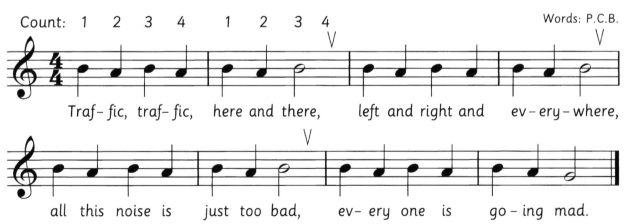

17 Traffic, traffic, here and there

Count: 1 2 3 4 1 2 3 4

Words: P.C.B.

Traf – fic, traf – fic, here and there, left and right and ev – ery – where,

all this noise is just too bad, ev – ery one is go – ing mad.

Look back at the song 'The hen' on page 28.

Add the time-signature and draw the bar-lines.

First duets

A piece of music in two parts is called a **duet** or **duo**.

When you are playing with someone else it is important
that each of you knows your own part really well.

Clap through the pieces first and then play them.

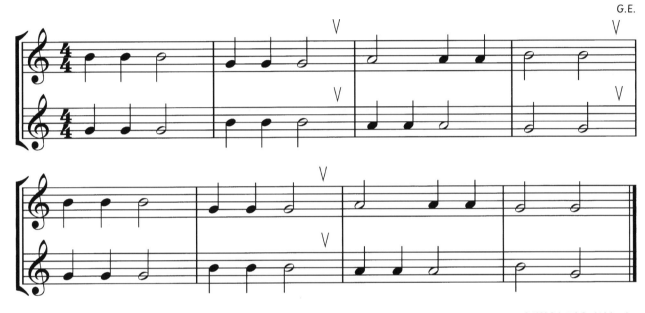

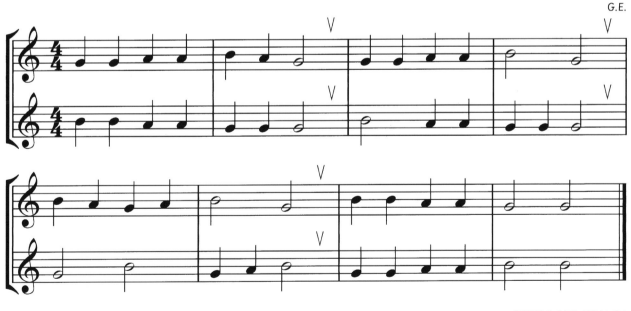

At home, play some pieces of music every day
and read the note names out loud.

You will find more pieces in Tune Book 1

c 20 Percussion piece   Count carefully throughout the piece.

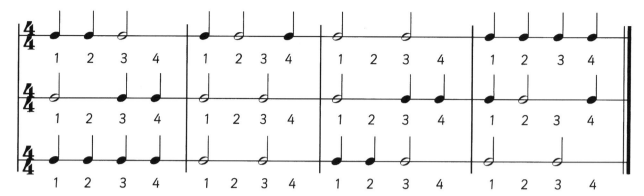

Compare the 'Percussion piece' with the following piece for three recorders.
A piece of music in three parts is called a **trio**.

21 Trio

G.E.

Above all, try to keep together!

Three-four time

In **three-four** time we count to three in each bar.
At the beginning of the piece we
write the time-signature, like this:

22 Teddy song

Music: G.E.
Words: P.C.B.

Ted – dy, ted – dy, stand on your head,

Ted – dy bear, ted – dy bear, go to bed.

Dotted minims

A minim is a note which lasts for two counts.

A dotted minim lasts for three counts, and is made by adding a dot (·) to a minim.

23 Melody

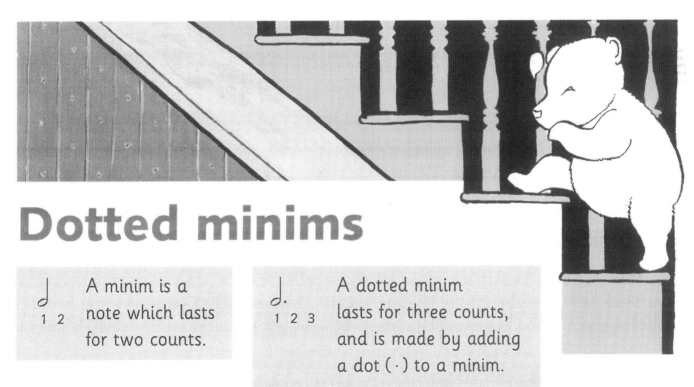

Three fairground songs in different time-signatures

24 Carousel and lemonade

Music: G.H.
Words: P.C.B.

© 1999 Schott & Co. Ltd, London

25 John at the fair

Music: G.H.
Words: P.C.B.

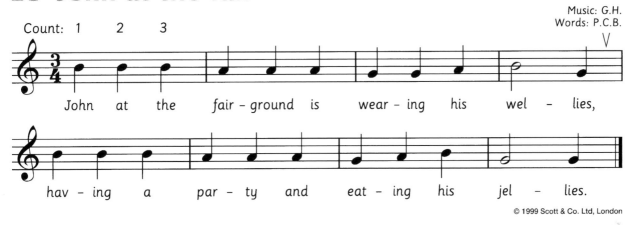

© 1999 Scott & Co. Ltd, London

In **two-four** time we count to two in each bar.
The time-signature is written like this: $\frac{2}{4}$

26 Sugar candy on a stick

Music: G.H.
Words: P.C.B.

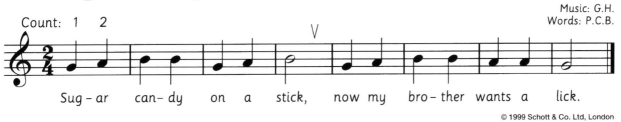

© 1999 Schott & Co. Ltd, London

Now the time-signature has been changed.
Try to write down the rest of the tune.

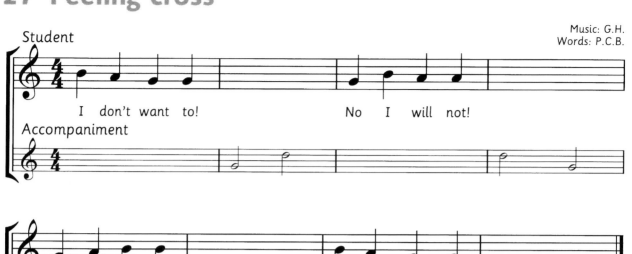

Music: G.H.
Words: P.C.B.

Student

I don't want to!   No I will not!

Accompaniment

I'll have no more!   No and that's that!

28 Feeling happy

Music: G.H.
Words: P.C.B.

Hey, hoo – ray   1   2   3

let's   go   out   run   a – bout!

29 Feeling tired

G.H.

hold as long as poss

Rests

c Sometimes in music there are silences between notes. These silences are called **rests**.

crotchet note

crotchet rest

minim note
1   2

minim rest
1   2

Write some crotchet rests and minim rests:

Now sing this song twice – first with all the words, then leaving out the word 'Jane'.

30 Song with rests

Music: G.E.
Words: P.C.B.

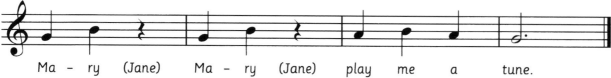

Ma – ry (Jane) Ma – ry (Jane) where's your re – cor – der?

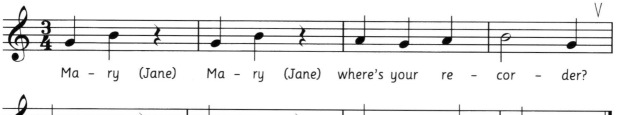

Ma – ry (Jane) Ma – ry (Jane) play me a tune.

31 Duet with rests

G.H.

32 Ball game

G.H.

C 33 Shoo, pussy, shoo!

Shoo, pus-sy, shoo, leave my gar-den, do.

Stalk a bird or chase a mouse. You'll find them round by

next-door's house. Just shoo, pus-sy, shoo!

T There are more pieces with piano accompaniment in Tune Book 1

The note E

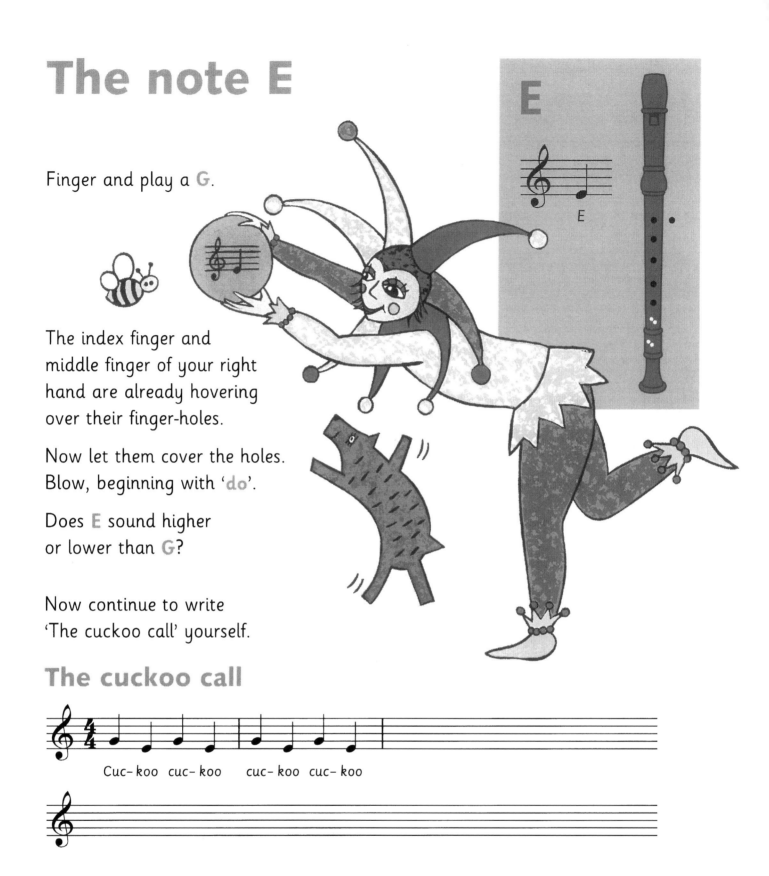

Finger and play a G.

The index finger and middle finger of your right hand are already hovering over their finger-holes.

Now let them cover the holes. Blow, beginning with 'do'.

Does E sound higher or lower than G?

Now continue to write 'The cuckoo call' yourself.

The cuckoo call

Cuc- koo cuc- koo   cuc- koo cuc- koo

34 G and E song

Oh! how hap-py   I   will   be   just   to   play   the   new note   E.

Make sure that the index and middle fingers of your right hand really do lift up and fall down together.

When you sing 'The drum', make the drum boom
by clapping your hands during the rests.

35 The drum

G.H.
Words: P.C.B.

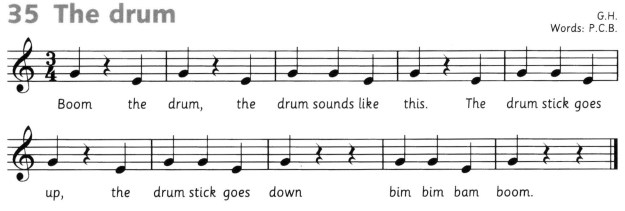

Boom   the   drum,   the   drum sounds like   this.   The   drum stick goes

up,   the   drum stick goes   down   bim bim bam boom.

How many fingers fall onto the finger-holes at the same time
when you change from **A** to **E**?

Music: German traditional
Words: P.C.B.

36 Adam was a naughty boy

A - dam was   a   naugh-ty   boy,   a   naugh-ty   boy was   A - dam.

He   would   al - ways   play   the   fool   and   frigh - ten   all   the

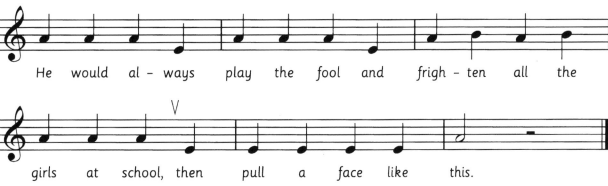

girls   at   school, then   pull   a   face   like   this.

37 Lonely shepherd

G.E.

38 Sad tune

G.H.

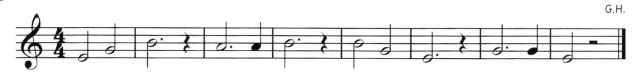

39 Happy tune

G.H.

At home, invent a melody and write it down.
Try to use all the notes that you know!

 Breathing exercise

Who can play the longest note?

Before you start to play, breathe in. Only your tummy should move –
it should get fatter. Don't raise your shoulders as you breathe in.

Play the note **E** for as long as you can. Remember to start with '**do**'
and play a firm, even note.

Follow along this line with your eyes as you blow...

With two friends, play these three notes.
Begin together and finish together:

Listening game

All stand back-to-back.

One of you plays either **G**, **E** or **B**.
The others find the missing notes
and join in to play them.

The up-beat

> The up-beat and the last bar together make one whole bar.

c Many pieces begin with a bar that is not complete. We call this an **up-beat**
Up-beats are played lightly and without emphasis.

Look closely at the last bar of 'The fire engine'.
What do you notice?

40 The fire engine

The   si – ren's   near.   The   fi – re   en – gine's   here!

41 Arctic dance

© 1999 Schott & Co. Ltd, London

44

The note C

First play a single long **A**.

Lift your index finger off the recorder. Now you are playing the note **C**.

Dotty-do-a-lot's finger game

Play an **A** and then let your index finger dance up and down on its finger-hole. Your tongue can have a rest because it just makes one long 'dooo'.

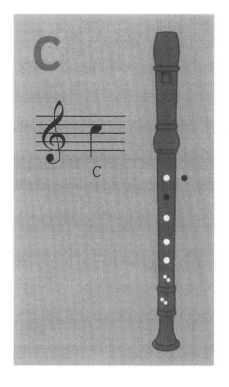

Your index finger can move quickly or slowly. Draw your finger dance in the space below.

C Finger dance

Name game

You can play finger dances to fit people's names – here are some:

Tim – o – thy   Nas – reen   Jen – ni – fer

An – to – ni – a   John

What are the names of the others in your group?
Sing and play their names with **C** and **A**. You can write them below.

42 TV song

Hel – lo Jen – ny, did you see that new pro–gramme on T V?

43 Tortoise, tortoise in your shell

Tor–toise, tor–toise in your shell. What a fun–ny place to dwell.

Tor–toise, tor toise in your shell. What a fun–ny place to dwell.

Fingers playing see-saws!

In order to play first a **B** and then a **C**, your index finger
and middle finger need to lift and fall like a see-saw.
When the middle finger falls, the index finger springs up!

First play very slowly. Then, just this once, watch your fingers:

44 On the see-saw

On the see–saw John and Jane, up down up down up a – gain.

Play it again, this time with one long '**dooo**':

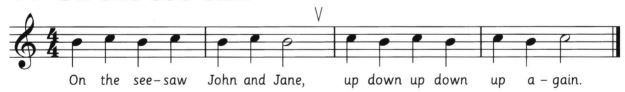

Both fingers must move at the same time.

Play 'The fire engine' again (see page 44), beginning this time on **G**. What is the second note? See if you can write out the whole tune.

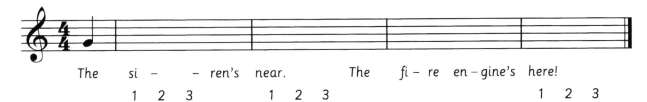

The   si –   – ren's   near.   The   fi – re en – gine's here!
        1   2   3   1   2   3   1   2   3

Finger exercises

T In **Tune Book 1** you will find some pieces with piano accompaniment.

Read out the note names of 'Question and answer', clapping at the same time. Now play the piece on your recorder.

48 Question and answer

1 2 3   1 2 3   1 2 3   1 2 3   1 2 3   1 2 3   1 2 3   1 2 3

Question   **Answer**

Invent your own 'Question and answer' and write it below.

The note D

Finger a **C** then lift your thumb off its hole.
Not too far – it must be able to find the
hole again quickly. The new note is called **D**.
Finger it without blowing.

Put your thumb back on its hole.
Feel carefully to make sure that the thumb
covers its hole properly. Play the notes
C and **D** slowly, one after another.

Now breathe in deeply and let your thumb
dance as you blow one long '**dooo**':

How many fingers are moving?

Here is 'On the see-saw' again,
but this time you play **B** and **D**.

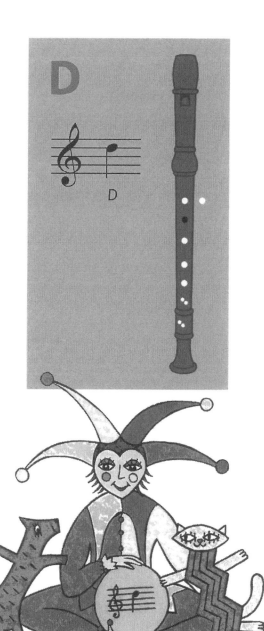

On the see-saw John and Jane, up down up down up a-gain.

49 D song

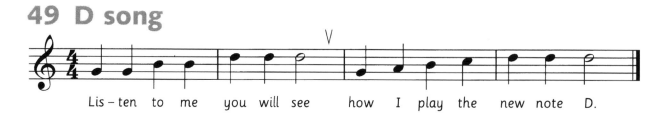

Lis-ten to me you will see how I play the new note D.

c Now alter the time-signature and play 'D song' in three-four time.
The first bars will look like this:

Lis – ten to me

Finish writing this song:

Nursery rhyme

50

Rain,   rain,   go   a – way,   come a – gain a – no – ther day.

1   2   3   4   1   2   3   4   1   2   3   4   1   2   3   4

Play 'The echo game' (see page 18) using the notes below.
Listen carefully: can you hear the difference between **B** and **C**?

E   G   A   B   C   D

Play the highest note and then the lowest.
Find out how loud you have to blow
to make each note sound good.

51 Curly locks

Nursery rhyme
Setting: P.C.B.

Cur– ly locks, cur– ly locks will you be mine? You shall not wash dish–es nor

yet feed the swine, but sit on a cu–shion and sew a fine seam and

feed up–on straw–ber–ries, su–gar and cream. Cur– ly locks, cur– ly locks

will you be mine? You shall not wash di–shes nor yet feed the swine.

T In **Tune Book 1** you will find lots of tunes that you are now able to play.

Canons

Before you play 'Creeping up the staircase', play
'Tortoise, tortoise in your shell' again (see page 46).

Notice that both people play the same music
but that one player begins one bar after
the other so that the music overlaps.

Music like this is called a **canon**.

The next two tunes are canons, too, but
this time each tune is written only once. The second
(and third) players start at the beginning when
the first player reaches the number 2 (and 3).

52 Creeping up the staircase

Words: P.C.B.

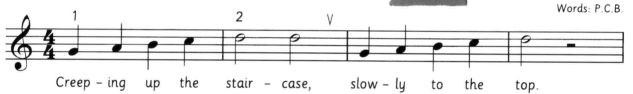

Creep - ing   up   the   stair - case,   slow - ly   to   the   top.

When   you   come   back   down   a - gain   just   hop,   hop,   hop,   hop,   hop.

53 Dance and sing

Words: W.L.

Dance   and   sing   and   jump   a - round. We   love   to   hear   the   mu - sic   sound.

54 Etude   An **étude** is a study or exercise piece.

G.H.

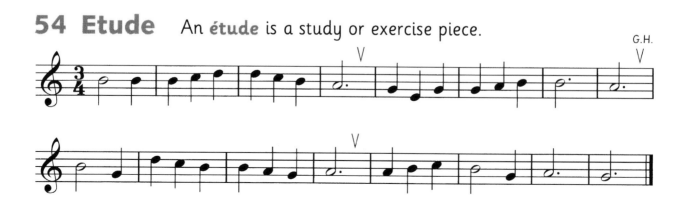

55 Little bird sits in the apple tree

German folk song
Words: P.C.B.

Student

Lit-tle bird sits in the ap-ple tree. Stays si-lent all the day long.

Accompaniment

On-ly at night do we hear him sing. That is the night-in-gale's song.

56 Cuckoo, cuckoo

German folk song
Words: P.C.B.

Cuc-koo, cuc-koo, voice sings so clear. We are all sing - ing,

sing-ing and danc - ing! Cuc - koo, cuc - koo, sum-mer draws near.

C Sounds around

With your recorder you can copy noises like hooting cars, revving engines, screeching brakes and whistling trains.

Invent a story using these noises and any others you can copy.

Screeching brakes

Howling

You can make this noise when the finger holes aren't properly covered.

You can make a howl by fingering a note while you cover and uncover the labium.

Hooting

Whistling train

You can make a hooting noise
by blowing with full cheeks
and all of the finger-holes open.

You can make a train's whistle
by partially covering the
labium while you finger a note.

57 Pat-a-cake

Nursery rhyme

Pat – a – cake, pat – a – cake, ba – ker's man, bake me a

cake as fast as you can. Prick it and pat it and

mark it with C and toss it up high for chil-dren like me.

58 Threshing song

Canon

Hear the three thre – shers they're thre – shing in time.

Clip clap clap, clip clap clap clip clap clip clap.

Accompaniments for songs 57 and 58

Percussion

Xylophone

Three notes sounding together

With two friends, breathe in together and start to play. Listen to how beautiful
it sounds. Make sure you all finish playing at the same time, too!

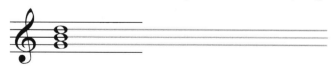

In **Tune Book 1** there are lots of songs and tunes that you can play.
Can you play the rest of this song from memory?

Good King Wen – ces – las looked out...

Index of tunes, songs and games

Goodbye everyone!
I hope you've had lots of fun.
I look forward to seeing you again in **Tutor Book 2** of **Fun and Games with the Recorder**.

Fingering chart

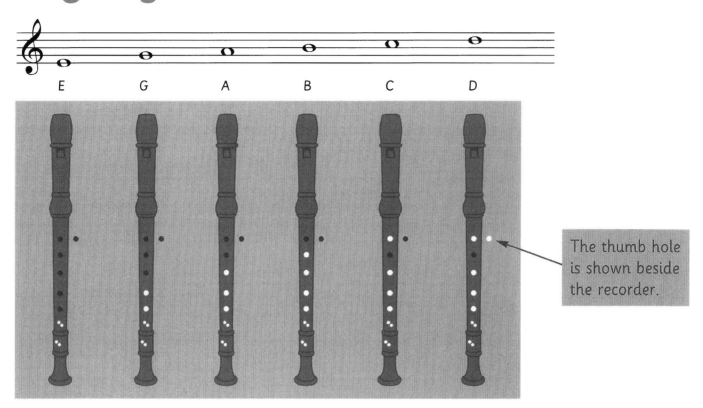

E   G   A   B   C   D

The thumb hole is shown beside the recorder.

Note values

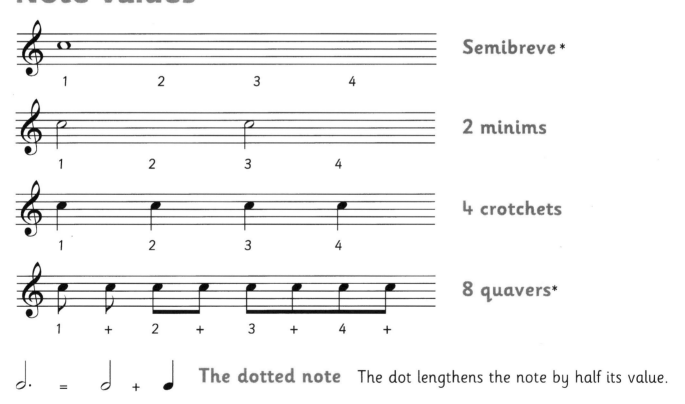

Semibreve *

2 minims

4 crotchets

8 quavers *

The dotted note   The dot lengthens the note by half its value.

Rests

Semibreve rest *   Minim rest   Crotchet rest   Quaver rest *

* You will find out about these things in **Tutor Book 2** of **Fun and Games with the Recorder**.

S&Co.80